WHATS NEW, BC.?

BY JOHNNY HART

A FAWCETT GOLD MEDAL BOOK

Fawcett Publications, Inc., Greenwich, Conn.

SEE THE FUNNY, FUNNY WALL.

SEE JANE JUMP THE WALL.

JANE HAS DEFECTED.

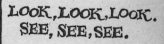

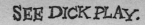

SEE DICK PLAY.

SEE DICK WORK.

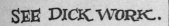

SEE SPOT WATCH
DICK WORK.

SPOT IS NO DOPE.

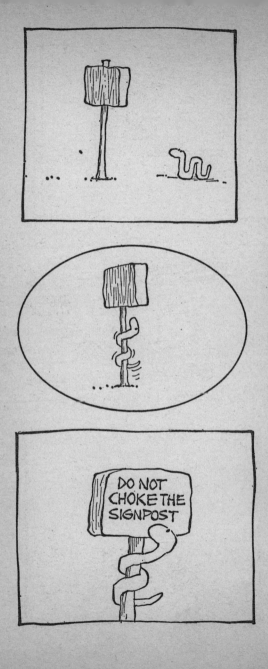

MAYBE IF WE SHAKE HIM —
WE CAN **SHAKE** OUT SOME IDEAS!

CLAMS!

SO FAR, THE BEST IDEA I'VE
HEARD WAS THE ONE TO
SHAKE HIM.

THE HECK WITH IDEAS.

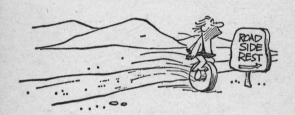

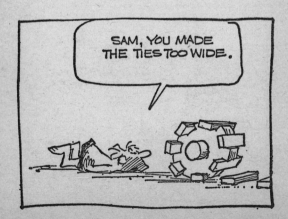

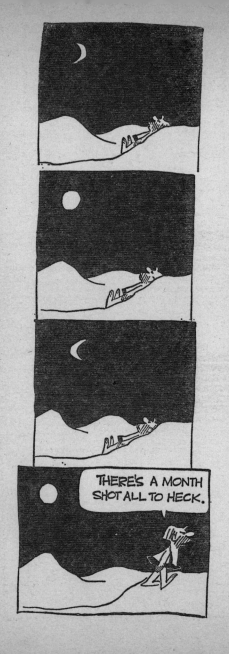

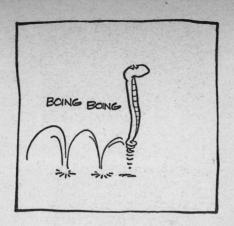

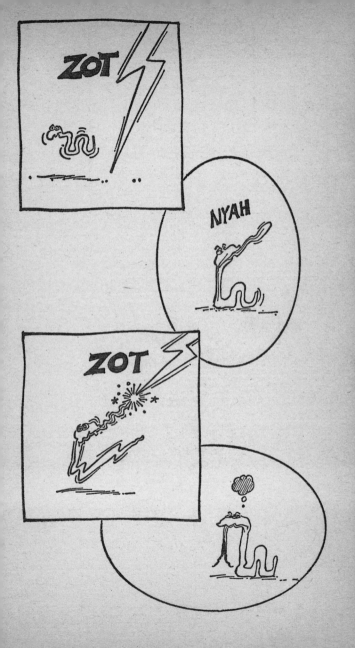

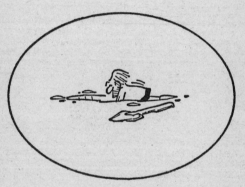

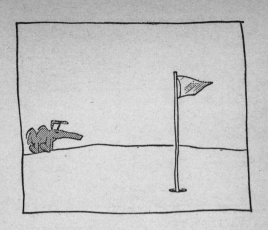

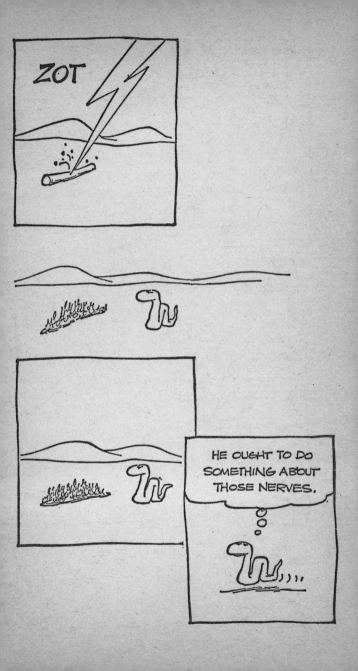

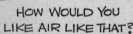

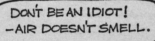

HOW WILL WE EVER DOMINATE OVER MAN ?
EASY ! — MARRY THEM.
YOU WANT WE SHOULD MARRY OUR NATURAL ENEMY ?
A MISERABLE MAN IS A VULNERABLE MAN.

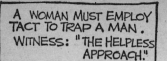

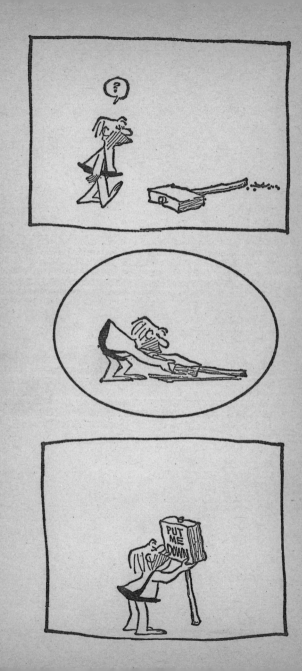